Piano
Grade 6

Pieces & Exercises
for Trinity College London exams

2015-2017

Published by
Trinity College London
www.trinitycollege.com

Registered in England,
Company no. 02683033
Charity no. 1014792

The Fall of the Leafe

from *The Fitzwilliam Virginal Book*

Martin Peerson
(1571/3-1651)

All musical indications are editorial

Andantino Grazioso

Second movement from Sonata in F

Jan Ladislav Dussek
(1760-1812)

4

[Blank page to facilitate page turns]

Sonatina

op. 36 no. 6

Muzio Clementi
(1752-1832)

Prayer of the Matador

from *Lyric Pieces for the Young*

Norman Dello Joio
(1913–2008)

Valse lente

Oskar Merikanto
(1868–1924)

Evocation

from *Variations sur un Thème de Chopin*

Federico Mompou
(1893-1987)

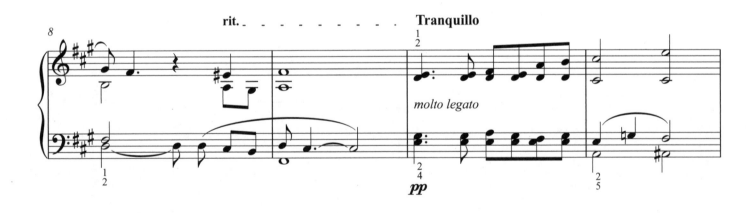

Jazzin' Grace

Garry A F Wilkinson
(born 1958)

The Wit and Wisdom of the Night

with a nod to Leonard Bernstein

Mark Tanner
(born 1963)

Castle Ward

Temple Dancer in Blue

June Armstrong
(born 1951)

With elegance and a hint of swing ♩ = c. **80–90**

Exercises

1a. Make it Fit! – tone, balance and voicing

1b. A Song – tone, balance and voicing

2a. Stubborn – co-ordination

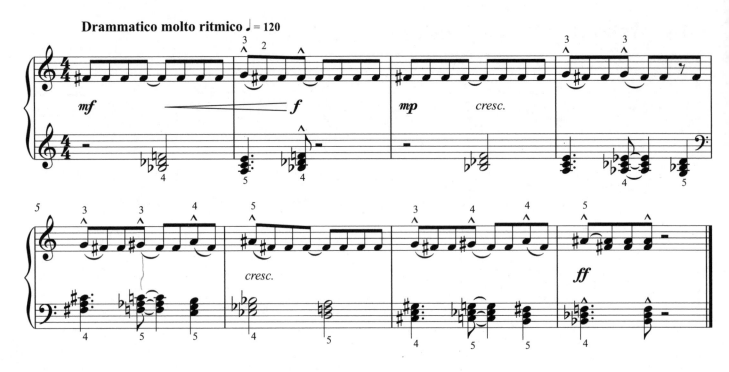

2b. Confused – co-ordination

3a. A Lucky Find – finger & wrist strength and flexibility

3b. Valse Triste – finger & wrist strength and flexibility

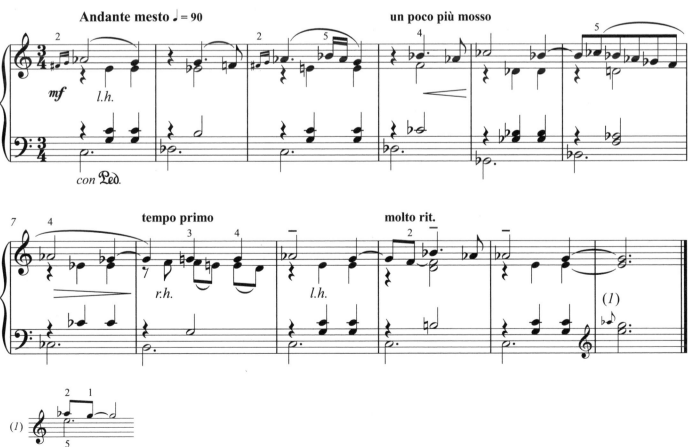